MUSICAL MEMOR

1940-19

WISE PUBLICATIONS
LONDON/NEW YORK/PARIS/SYDNEY/COPENHAGEN/MADRID

EXCLUSIVE DISTRIBUTORS:

MUSIC SALES LIMITED
8/9 FRITH STREET, LONDON W1V 5TZ, ENGLAND.

MUSIC SALES PTY LIMITED
120 ROTHSCHILD AVENUE, ROSEBERY, NSW 2018, AUSTRALIA.

ISBN 0-7119-0021-3/ORDER NO. AM30149

ART DIRECTION BY MIKE BELL
DESIGNED BY CARROLL & DEMPSEY LIMITED

PRINTED IN THE UNITED KINGDOM BY
J.B. OFFSET PRINTERS (MARKS TEY) LIMITED, MARKS TEY, ESSEX.

CHATTANOOGA CHOO-CHOO

WORDS BY
MACK GORDON

MUSIC BY
HARRY WARREN

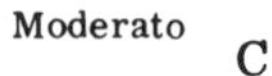

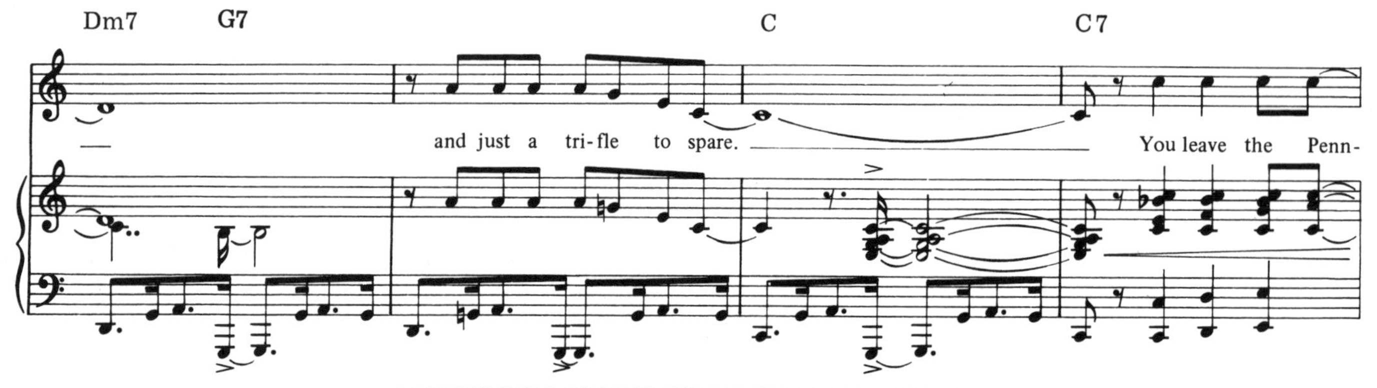

F
C7
F
C7
F
F9
- syl - va - nia sta - tion 'bout a quar-ter to four, read a mag - a - zine and then you're in Bal - ti - more, Din-

B♭
F°
F
D7
G7-9
A♭m6
- ner in the din - er noth - ing could be fin - er than to have your ham - 'n eggs in Car - o - li - na. When

F
C7
F
C7
F
C7
F
you hear the whis-tle blow-in' eight to the bar Then you know that Ten-nes-see is not ve-ry far, Shov-

B♭
F°
F
D7
G7-9
C7
F
- el all the coal in, got - ta keep it roll - in' Woo, Woo, Chat - ta - noo - ga there you are.

C
There's gon-na be a cer - tain par - ty at the
mp

Dm7 G7
sta - tion
Sat - in and lace,
I used to call fun - ny face.

C
C7
She's gon - na cry
un-til I tell her that I'll

F
A♭7
D7
C
Am7
D7
Dm7
nev-er roam,
So
Chat - ta - noo - ga Choo-choo won't you choo - choo me home.

C
Cm6
C7
Cm6
Chat -

C7
Am7
D7
Dm7
C
- ta - noo - ga Choo-choo Won't you choo - choo me home.
sfz

LAURA

WORDS BY
JOHNNY MERCER

MUSIC BY
DAVID RAKSIN

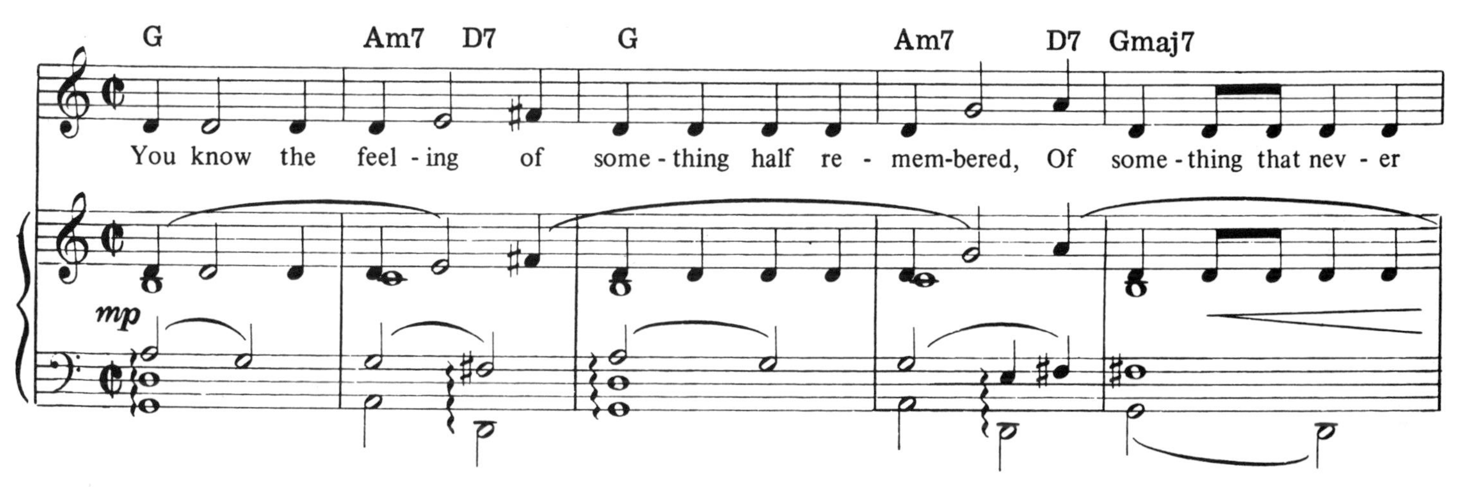

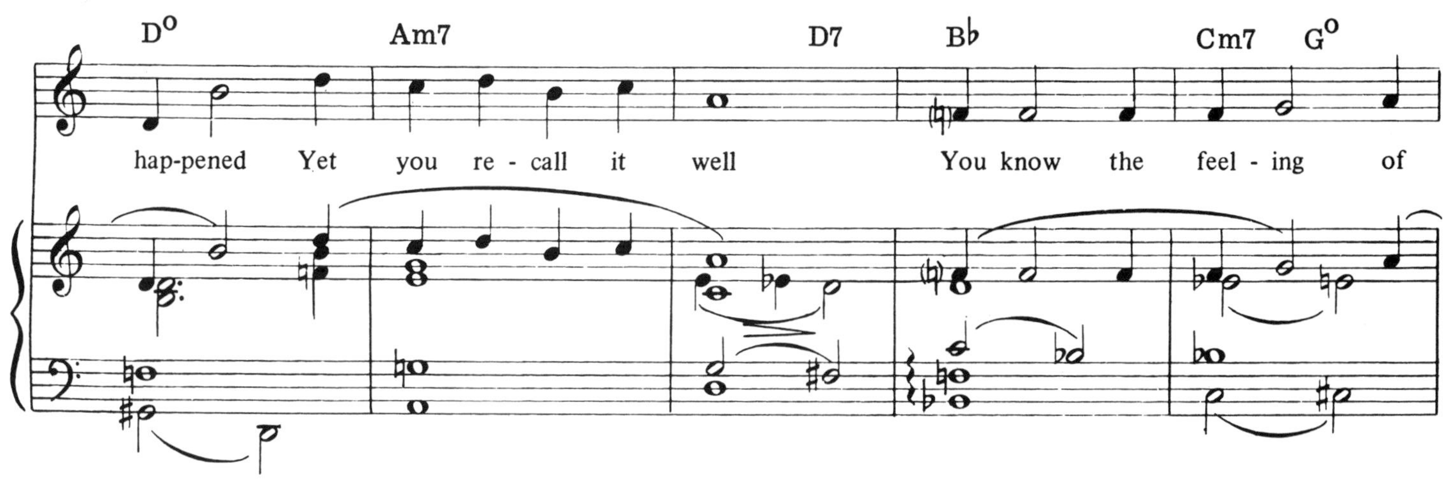

Slowly with expression

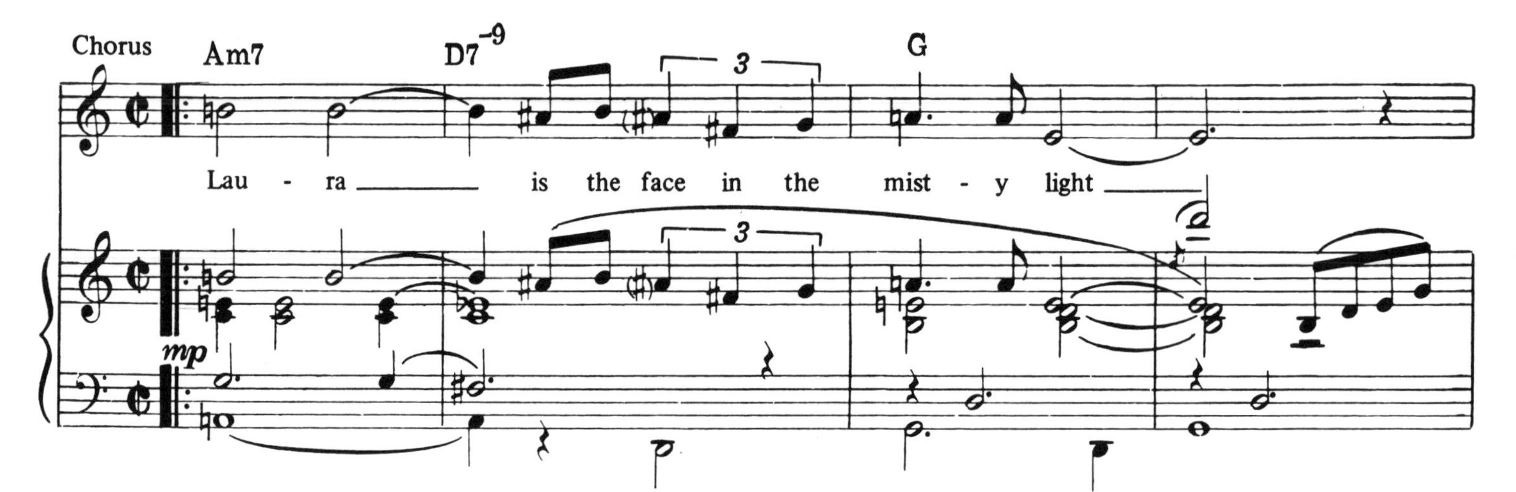

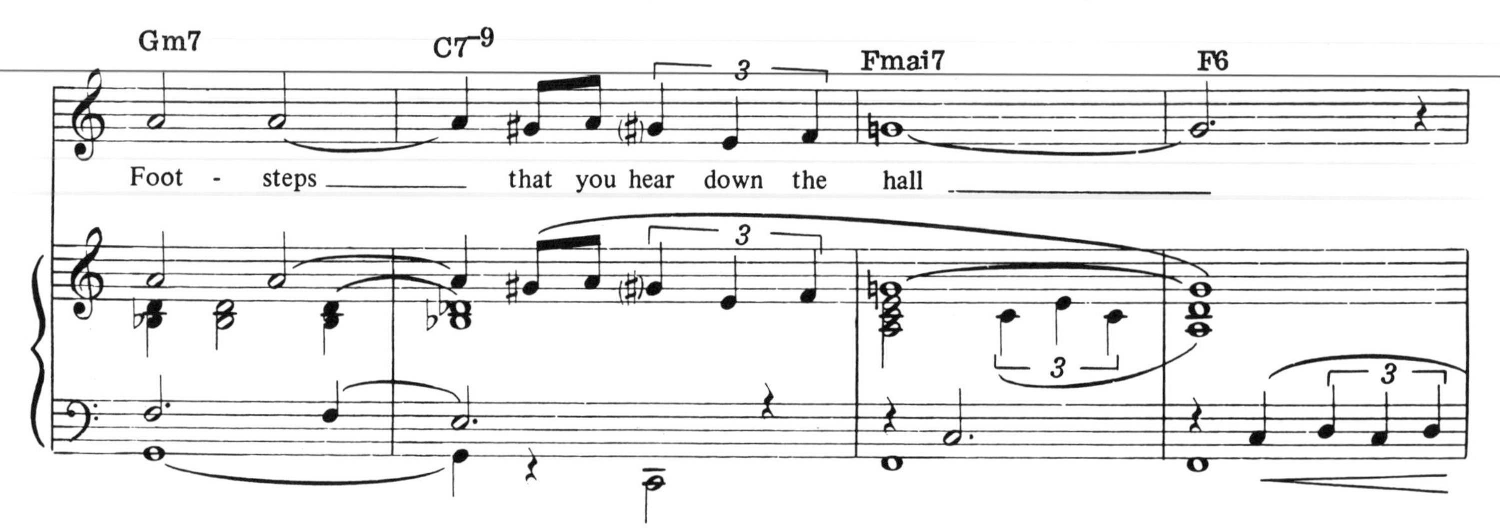

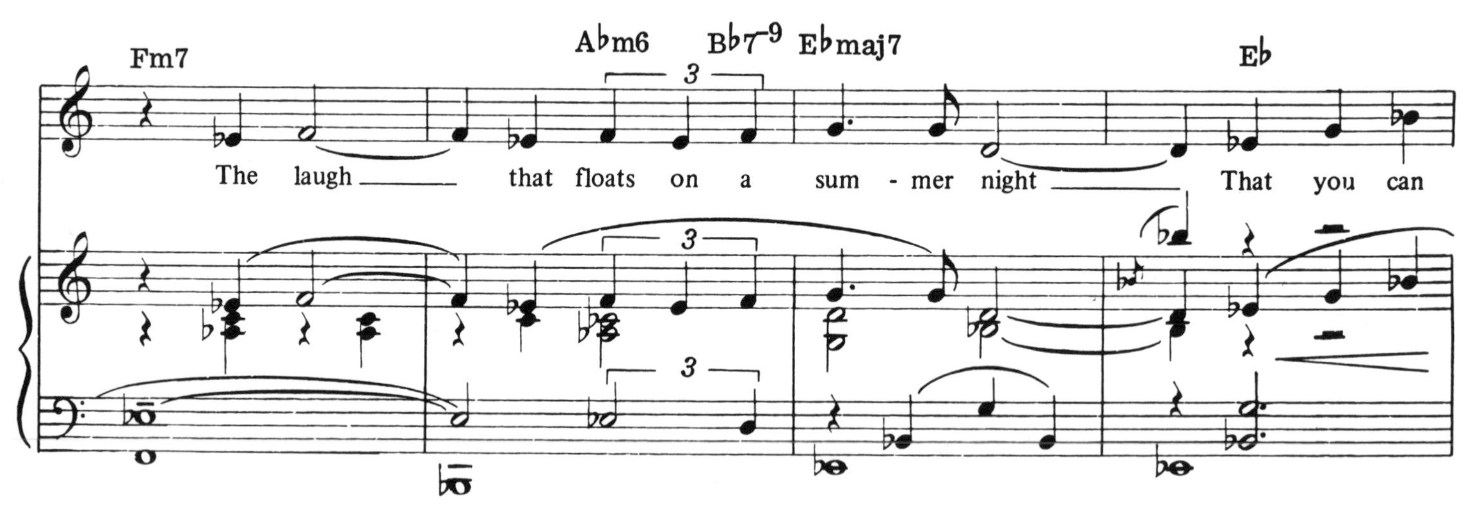

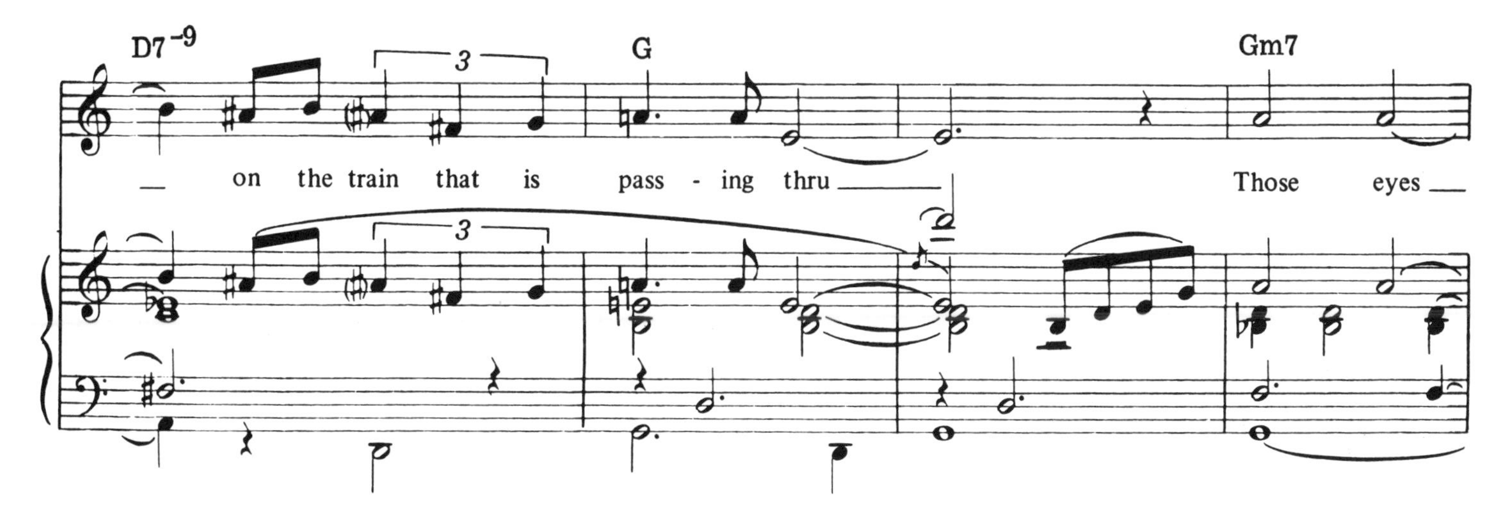
D7-9
3
G
Gm7
— on the train that is pass - ing thru ——
Those eyes —

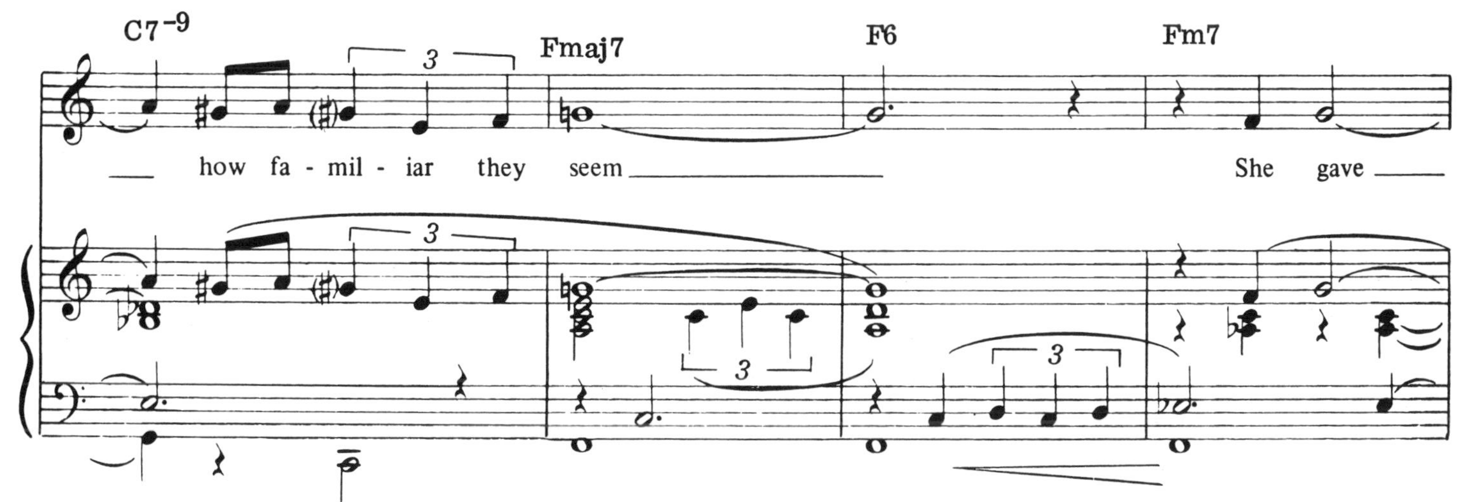
C7-9
3
Fmaj7
F6
Fm7
— how fa - mil - iar they seem ——
She gave ——

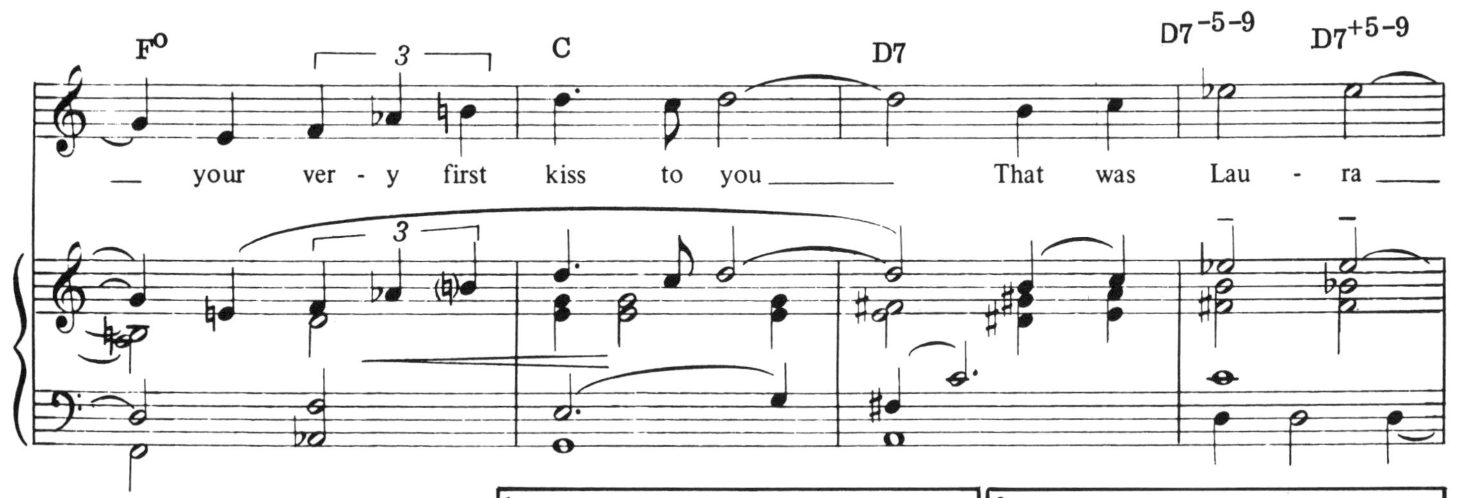
F°
3
C
D7
D7-5-9
D7+5-9
— your ver - y first kiss to you ——
That was Lau - ra ——

G9
G7-9
1.
C
E9
E7-9
2.
C
— but she's on - ly a dream.
dream. ——
rall.
p

MIDNIGHT SUN

WORDS BY
JOHNNY MERCER

MUSIC BY
SONNY BURKE & LIONEL HAMPTON

A♭
star its own au - ro - ra bo - re - a - lis, sud - den - ly you
A♭m7
D♭9(♭5)
Cmaj7
Am7
held me tight, I could see the mid - night sun.
Dm7
G7-9
C
I can't ex - plain the sil - ver rain that found me, or was that a
Cm7
F9(♭5)
Cm7
F9(♭5)
F9
B♭
moon - lit veil? The mu - sic of the un - i - verse a -

Bbm7
Eb9(b5)
Eb9
round me, or was that a night - in - gale? And
Ab
then your arms mi - ra - cu - lous - ly found me, sud - den - ly the
Abm7
Db9(b5)
Db9
Cmaj7
C6
sky turned pale, I could see the mid-night sun.
F#m7
B13(b9)
Emaj7
E6
Em7
A13
A7+
Was there such a night, it's a thrill I still don't quite be -

Dmaj7
D6
Dmaj7
D6
Dmaj7
D6
lieve, ___ But af - ter you were gone, there was
Dm7
G13
G7+
Em7
E♭9
Dm9
D♭9(9+)
still some star-dust on my sleeve. ___ The
C
flame of it may dwin - dle to an em - ber, and the stars for -
Cm7
F9(♭5)
Cm7
F9(♭5)
F9
B♭
get to shine, ___ And we may see the mea - dow in De-

Bbm7
Eb9(b5)
Eb9
cem-ber, ic - y white and crys - tal - line. But,
Ab
oh, my dar - ling al - ways I'll re - mem - ber, when your lips were
Abm7
Db9(b5)
1 Cmaj7
C
close to mine, And I/we saw the mid-night sun.
Dm7
G7-9
2 Cmaj7
C
Db9(b5)
C13
Your mid-night sun.

YOURS

ENGLISH WORDS BY
JACK SHERR

MUSIC BY
GONZALO ROIG.

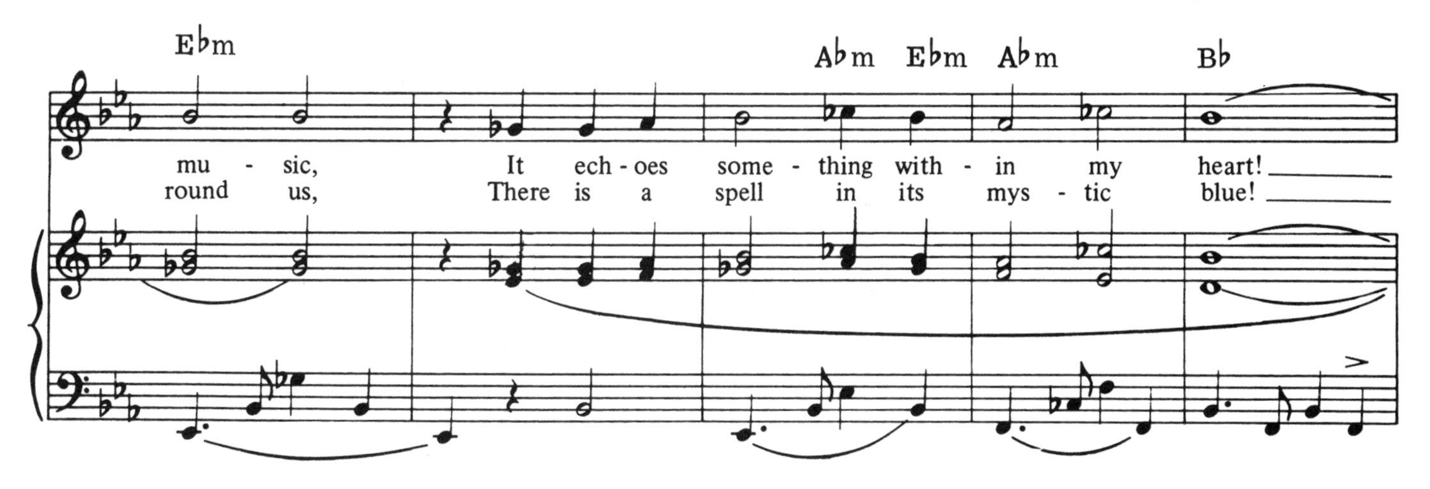

B♭7
1 E♭m
2 E♭
mes - sage I must im - part The cloak of
of - fer my all to you.

E♭ E♭o A♭ E♭
Yours till the stars lose their glo - ry! Yours till the

C7 Fm Fm7
birds fail to sing! Yours to the end of life's

B♭7 Fm B♭7 E♭
sto - ry, This pledge to you, dear, I bring!

E♭
E♭o
A♭
E♭
E♭7
Yours in the grey of De - cem - ber

C7
Fm
Here or on far dis - tant shores!
I've ne - ver

Fm7
A♭
E♭7
Eo
Fm
C7
Fm
A♭m
loved an - y - one the way I love you! How could I?
When I was

E♭
B♭7
1
E♭
B♭7
2
E♭
born to be just yours!
yours!

I CAME, I SAW, I CONGA'D

WORDS & MUSIC BY
JAMES CAVANAUGH, JOHN REDMOND
& FRANK WELDON

G6
to it And so I gave the Con - ga a try.
F9
F7
B♭
Gm7
F7
Gm7
C9
F7
Yi yi yi yi yi yi yi yi.
CHORUS
Dm
E♭
Dm
Cm
B♭
F9
F7
B♭
F7
Gm
F
B♭6
I came, I saw, I con - ga'd. I came, I saw, I con - ga'd; It's
p–f
sfz
sfz
sfz
sfz
B♭/D
B♭dim
F7
Cm7
F7
B♭
Dm
plain to see you con - quered me. Each

Eb
Dm
Cm
Bb
F9
F7
Bb
F7
Gm
F
Bb6
time I shake a shoul - der, I get a lit - tle bold - er. A
sfz
sfz
sfz
sfz
Bb/D
Bbdim
F7
Cm7
F7
Bb
D
dance like this de - serves a kiss. My
A7
sweet mu - cha - cha, when I got - cha
3
3
3
3
D
F
in my arms. This

C7
— Cu - ban hot - cha adds so mu - cha
F7 Ebm6 F7 Dm Eb Dm Cm Bb
— to your charms. The bon - gos beat the
F9 F7 Bb F7 Gm F Bb6 Bb/D Bbdim
rhy - thm, — Ma - ra - cas shake it with 'em, — That Lat - in
F7 Cm7 F7 Bb Dm Eb Dm Cm Bb
riff is too "ter - iff"; I came, I saw, I
sfz sfz sfz sfz

F9 F7 Bb F7 Gm F Bb6 Bb/D Bbdim
con - ga'd, I came, I saw, I con - ga'd; I can't de -
sfz sfz sfz sfz
F7 Cm7 F7 Bb C9 F7
ny, It's got that I, yi, Con - ga,
Bb C9 F7 Bb C9 F7
I, yi, Con - ga, I, yi, Con - ga,
1 Bb6 F7 Dm 2 Bb6
yi. I yi.
ff

ONCE IN LOVE WITH AMY

WORDS & MUSIC BY
FRANK LOESSER

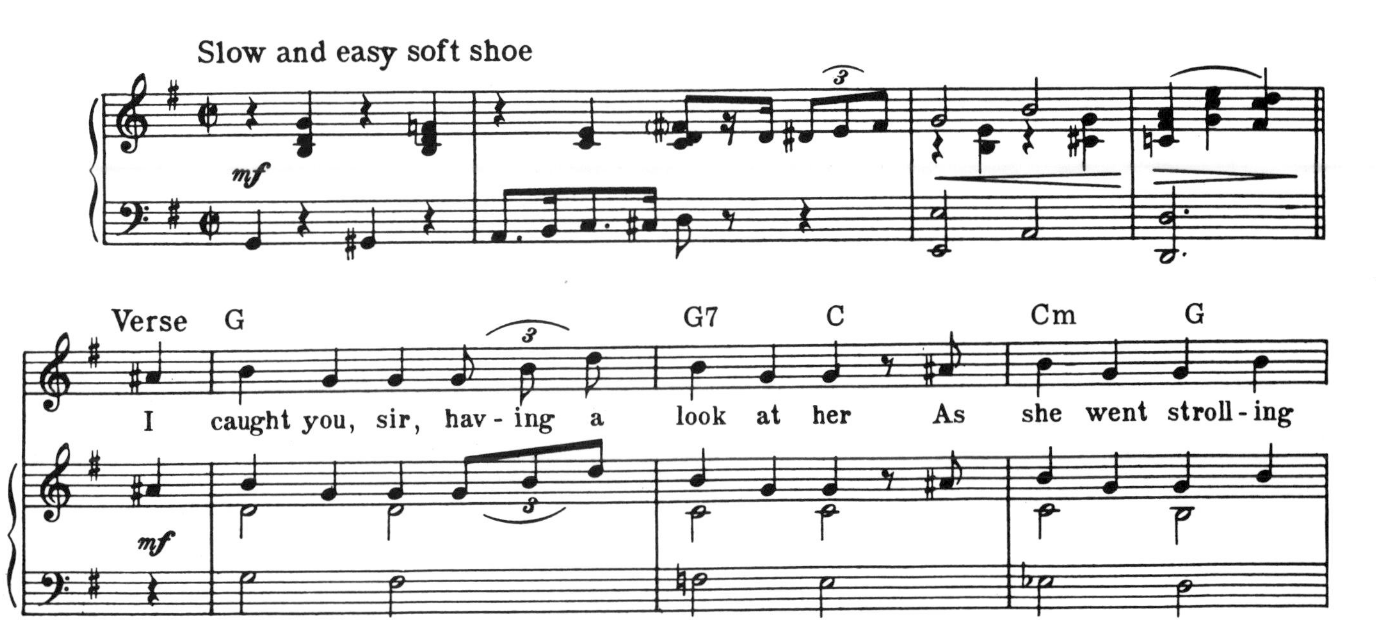

Am7
D7
Em7
A7
D7
boom, boom, boom, boom, boom, Boom, boom, boom, boom ___ from then on, For

Chorus
G
G#o
D7
G
G#o
D7
ONCE IN LOVE WITH A - MY, ___ Al-ways in love with A - my. ___
mp

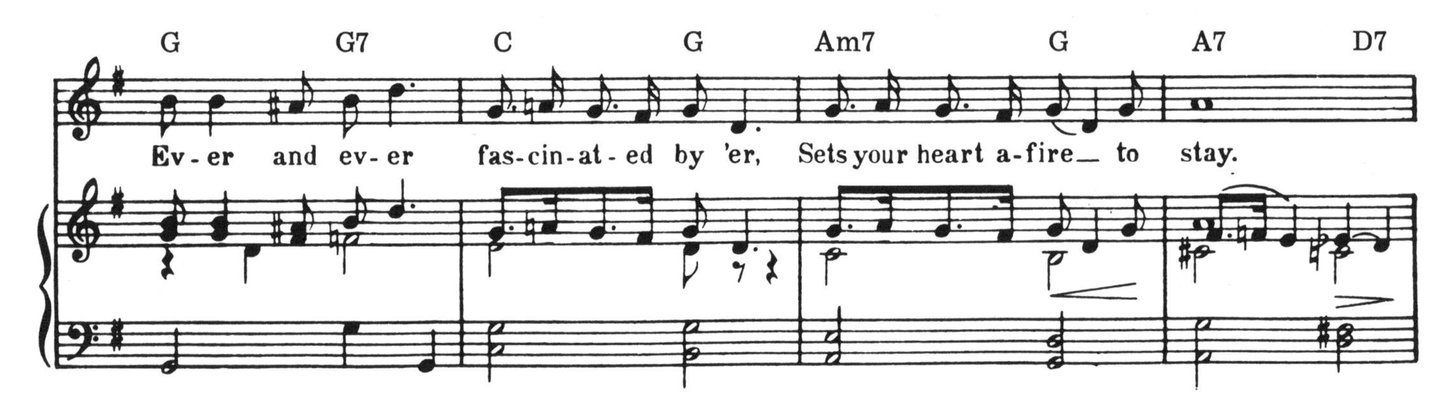
G
G7
C
G
Am7
G
A7
D7
Ev - er and ev - er fas-cin-at - ed by 'er, Sets your heart a-fire ___ to stay.

G
G#o
D7
G
G#o
D7
Once you're kissed by A - my, ___ Tear up your list, it's A - my. ___

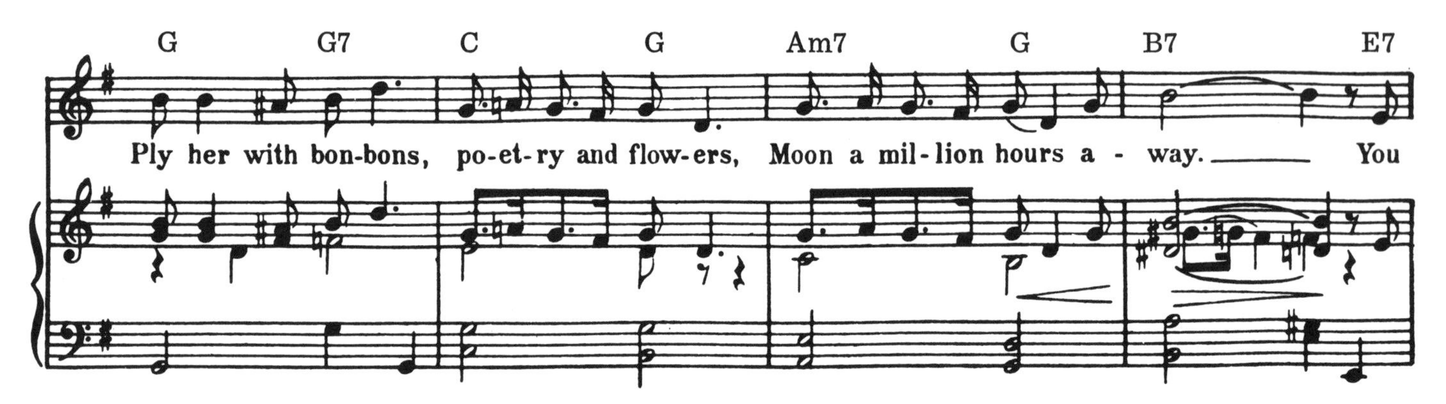
G
G7
C
G
Am7
G
B7
E7
Ply her with bon-bons, po-et-ry and flow-ers, Moon a mil-lion hours a - way. ___ You

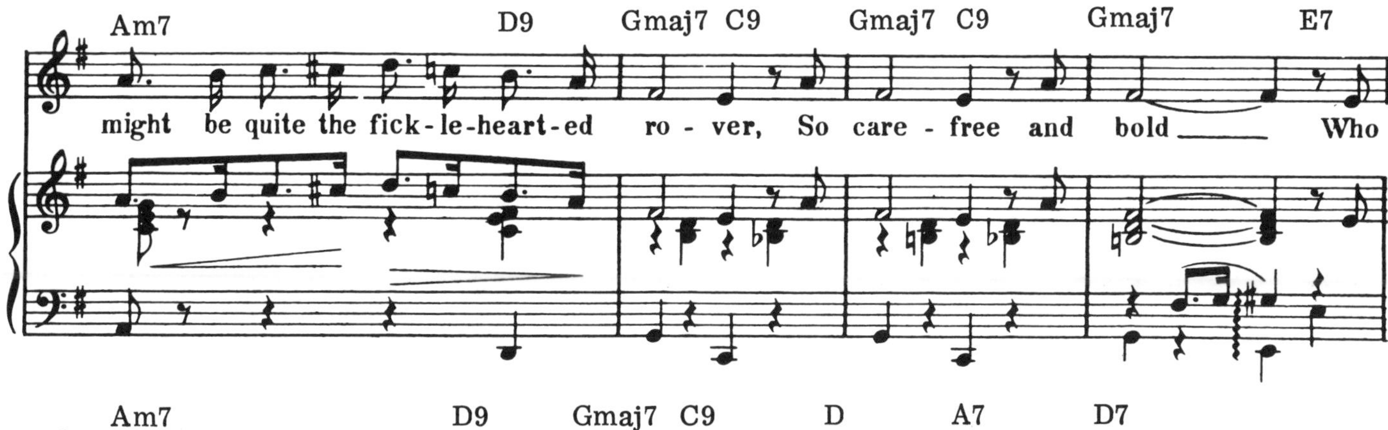
Am7 D9 Gmaj7 C9 Gmaj7 C9 Gmaj7 E7
might be quite the fick-le-heart-ed ro - ver, So care - free and bold Who

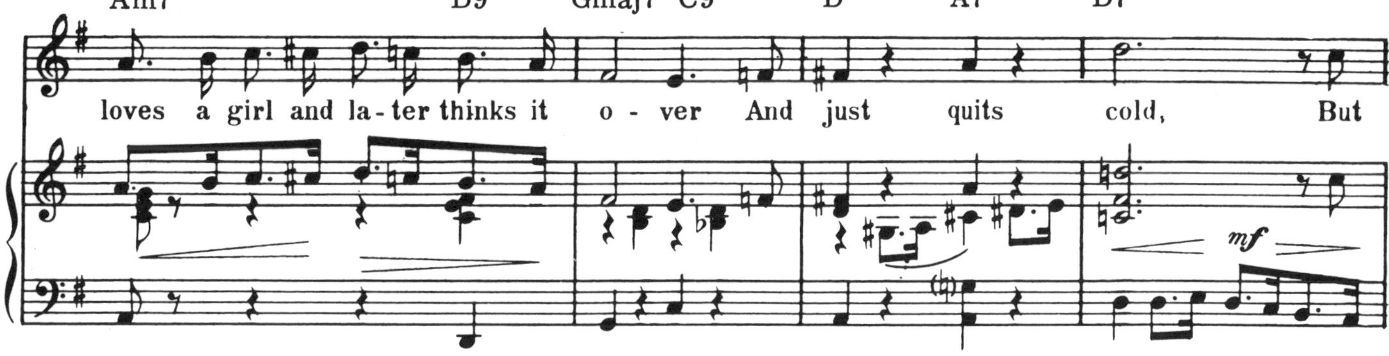
Am7 D9 Gmaj7 C9 D A7 D7
loves a girl and la-ter thinks it o - ver And just quits cold, But
mf

G F° D7 G F° D7 G G7
ONCE IN LOVE WITH A-MY, Al-ways in love with A - my. Ev-er and ev-er
mp

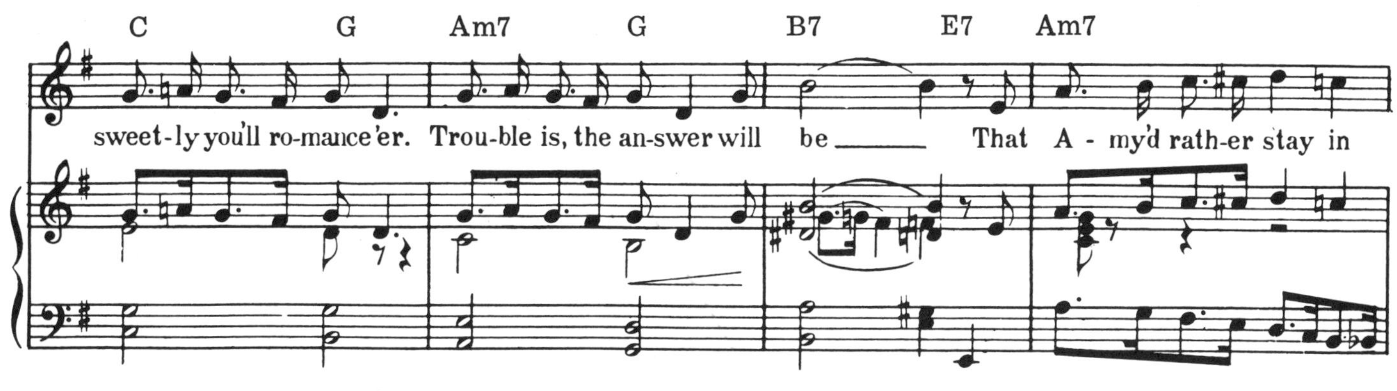
C G Am7 G B7 E7 Am7
sweet-ly you'll ro-mance 'er. Trou-ble is, the an-swer will be That A - my'd rath-er stay in

A9 D7 1 G Am7 D7 2 G
love with me. me.
mf
p

THAT OLE DEVIL CALLED LOVE

WORDS & MUSIC BY
DORIS FISHER & ALLAN ROBERTS

CHORUS
a tempo
Fm7
C7 (♭9 ♭5)
Fm7
B♭7
B♭7+
It's That Ole Devil Called Love a - gain. Gets be -
a tempo
E♭maj7
D7+
A♭7
Gm7
C9
Cm7 /F
F9
hind me and keeps giv-ing me that shove a-gain Put-ting rain in my eyes,
B9 (♭5)
B♭9
A♭dim
Gm
E♭ /G
F♯dim
Fm7
B♭7 (♭5)
B♭7
Tears in my dreams, and rocks in my heart. It's that
Fm7
C7 (♭9 ♭5)
Fm7
B♭7
B♭7+
E♭maj7
D7+
A♭7
sly son-of-a-gun a-gain, He keeps tell-ing me that I'm the luck-y

Gm7
C9
Cm7
/F
F9
B7
(♭5)
B♭9
one a-gain But I still — have the rain, Still — have those tears and those
E♭
A♭
Gm7
F♯m7
B9
Fm7
B♭9
rocks in my heart — Sup-pose I did-n't stay, —
Gm7
C7+
(♭9)
Fm7
Fm7
/B♭
E7
(+9)
ran a-way, — would-n't play, — that dev-il what a po-tion he would
E♭
Dm7
G7
(♭5)
A♭
/C
G
/B♮
Cm
brew — He'd fol-low me a-round, — build me up, — tear me down, — Til

Cm7
/F
F7
(♭9)
Fm7
E
/B♭
Fm7
C7
(♭9 ♭5)
I'd be so be-wil-dered, I would-n't know what to do. Might as well give up the
Fm7
B♭7
B♭7+
E♭maj7
D7+
A♭7
Gm7
C9
fight a-gain, I know darn well he'll con-vince me that he's right a-gain, When he
Cm7
/F
F9
B9
(♭5)
B♭9
Tacet
Fm7
Fm7
/B♭
E7
(+9)
sings that si-ren song I just got-ta tag a-long with That Ole Dev-il Called
E♭
A♭7
G7
(♭9)
C7
(♭9)
E♭
A♭
G7
(+9)
C7
(+9)
F7
Emaj7
E♭
Love. It's that Love.

YOU ALWAYS HURT THE ONE YOU LOVE

WORDS & MUSIC BY
DORIS FISHER & ALLAN ROBERTS

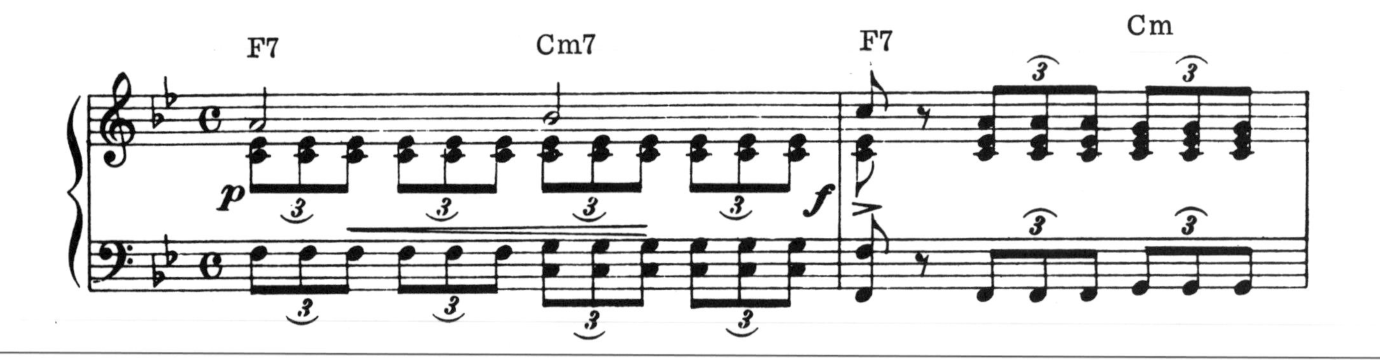

B♭
F7
B♭7
E♭
fall.
You al - ways break the kind - est

G°
C7
Cm7
F9
F7
heart, With a hast-y word you can't re - call
So

B♭
G7
C7
if I broke your heart last night, It's be - cause I love you

Cm7
F13-9
1 B♭
Cm7
F7
2 B♭
Cm7
B♭6
most of all
You
all.

NOW IS THE HOUR

WORDS BY
MAEWA KALHAU

MUSIC BY
CLEMENT SCOTT

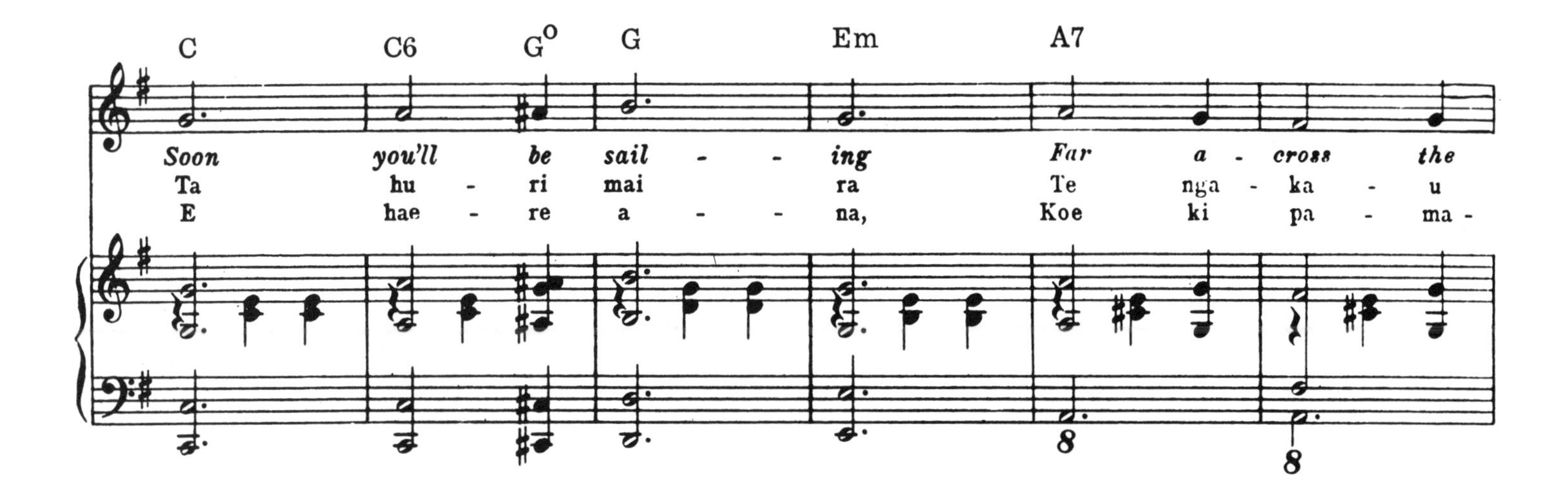
C C6 G° G Em A7
Soon you'll be sail - - ing Far a - cross the
Ta hu - ri mai ra Te nga - ka - u
E hae - re a - - - na, Koe ki pa - ma -
8
8

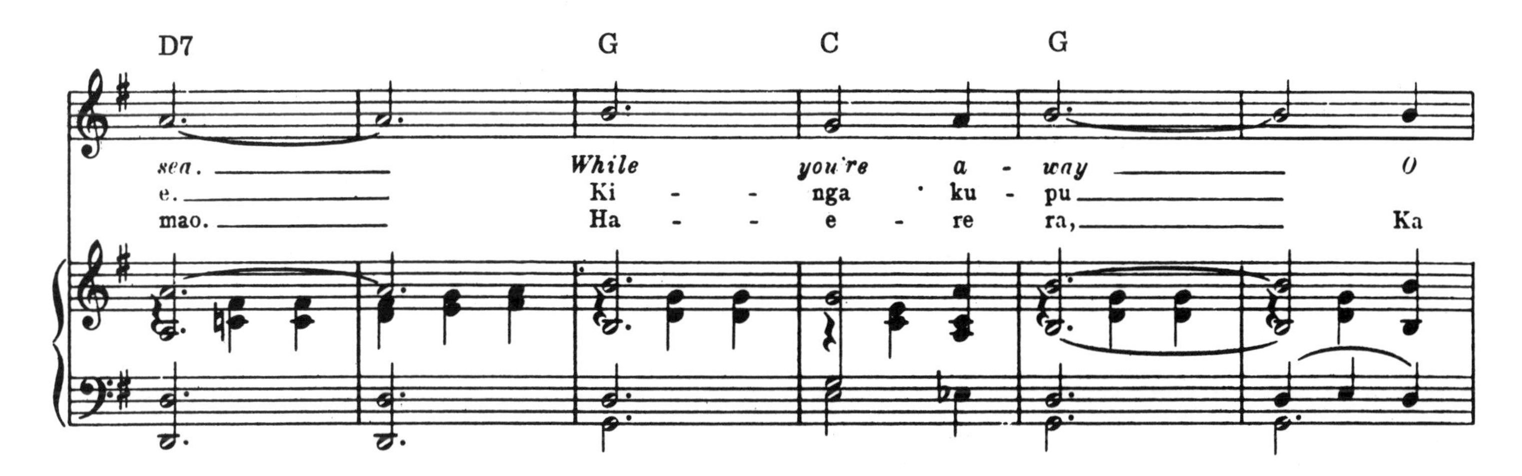
D7 G C G
sea. While you're a - way O
e. Ki - - nga ku - pu
mao. Ha - - e - re ra, Ka

D7 G C C6 G°
please re - mem - ber me, When you re -
O - te ro - ngo pai, Hei o - ra -
ho - ki mai a - no, Ki - - te
cresc.

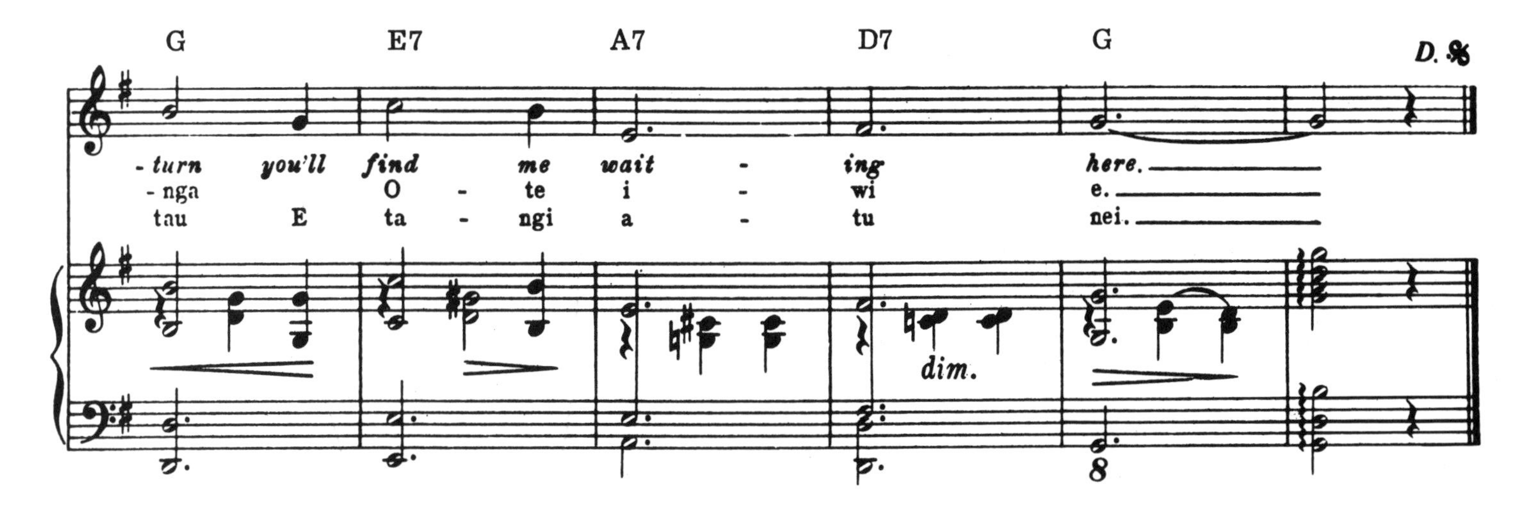
G E7 A7 D7 G
D.S.
- turn you'll find me wait - ing here.
- nga O - te i - wi e.
tau E ta - ngi a - tu nei.
dim.
8

ON A SLOW BOAT TO CHINA

WORDS & MUSIC BY
FRANK LOESSER

Bb Dm7 G7 Cm C#o Bb D7
Out on the briny with a moon big and shin-y, Melt-ing your heart of
mf

Eb Cm Fm Cm7 Ab7 A7 Bb Ab7
stone, I'd love to get you On a slow boat to
f

G7 C7 Cm7 B7 Bb Cm7 F+
Chi-na, All to my-self a - lone.

2 To Interlude
3 Fine
Bb Bb Cm7 Bb6
-lone. There is no -lone.
mf
ff

INTERLUDE
Bb Eb Eo Bb Eo Eb F7
verse to this song, 'Cause I don't want to wait a moment too long To say that
Back to Refrain

DEARLY BELOVED

WORDS BY
JOHNNY MERCER

MUSIC BY
JEROME KERN

Cmaj7 C#o Am7 Em A♭9 A♭7
An - gel voic - es led me to you;
G F G F
Noth - ing could save me, Fate gave me a sign;
G Dm7 G G9
I know that I'll be yours come show - er or shine;
C D7 G7 Dm
So I say mere - ly, Dear - ly be -
Dm7 G7 1 C B♭7 2 C
lov - ed be mine.
mine.

SKYLARK

WORDS BY
JOHNNY MERCER

MUSIC BY
HOAGY CARMICHAEL

Eb Gm Ab Eb Ab Eb
green with spring, Where my heart can go a - jour-ney - ing

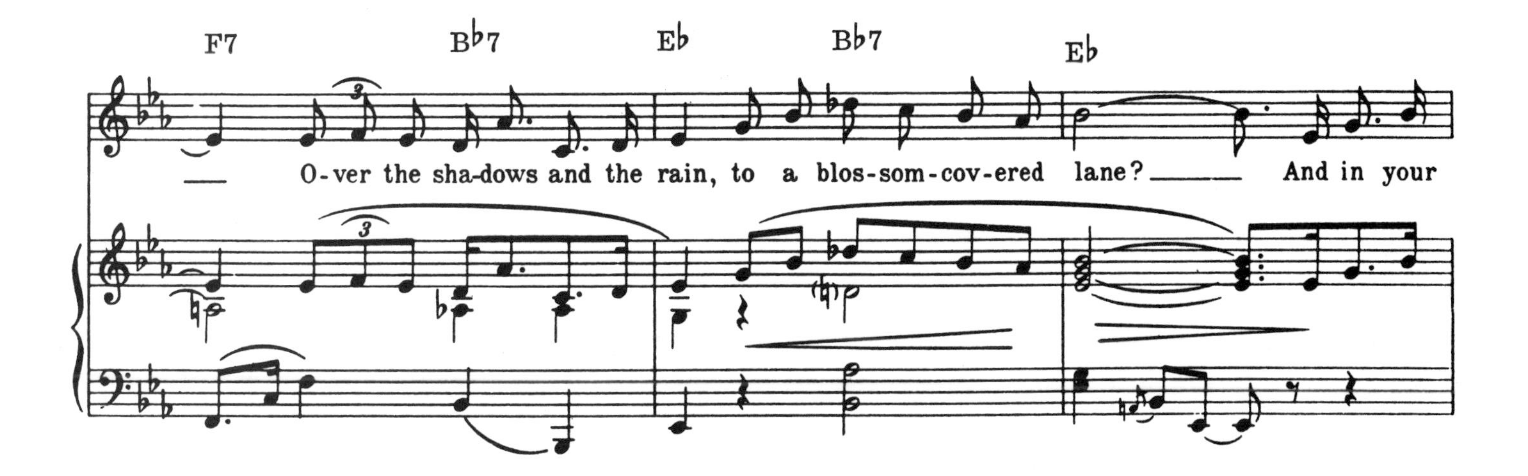
F7 Bb7 Eb Bb7 Eb
O-ver the sha-dows and the rain, to a blos-som-cov-ered lane? And in your

Ab Eb6 Fm7 Eb7 Ab Eb° Ab6
lone-ly flight Have-n't you heard the mu-sic in the night,

C7 D° C7 Fm F° Db Fm Eb7 Ab
Won-der-ful mu-sic, Faint as a will o' the wisp, Cra - zy as a loon,

G
A7
D7
G
Bb7
Sad as a gyp - sy se - re - nad - ing the moon. Oh,

Eb6
Bb7
Eb
Ab
Eb
Gm
Sky - lark, I don't know if you can find these things,

Ab
Eb
Ab
Eb
F7
Bb7
But my heart is rid - ing on your wings; So if you see them an - y -

Eb
Bb7
1
Eb
Bb9
2
Eb
Eb6
- where, Won't you lead me there? there?

FOOLS RUSH IN

WORDS BY
JOHNNY MERCER

MUSIC BY
RUBE BLOOM

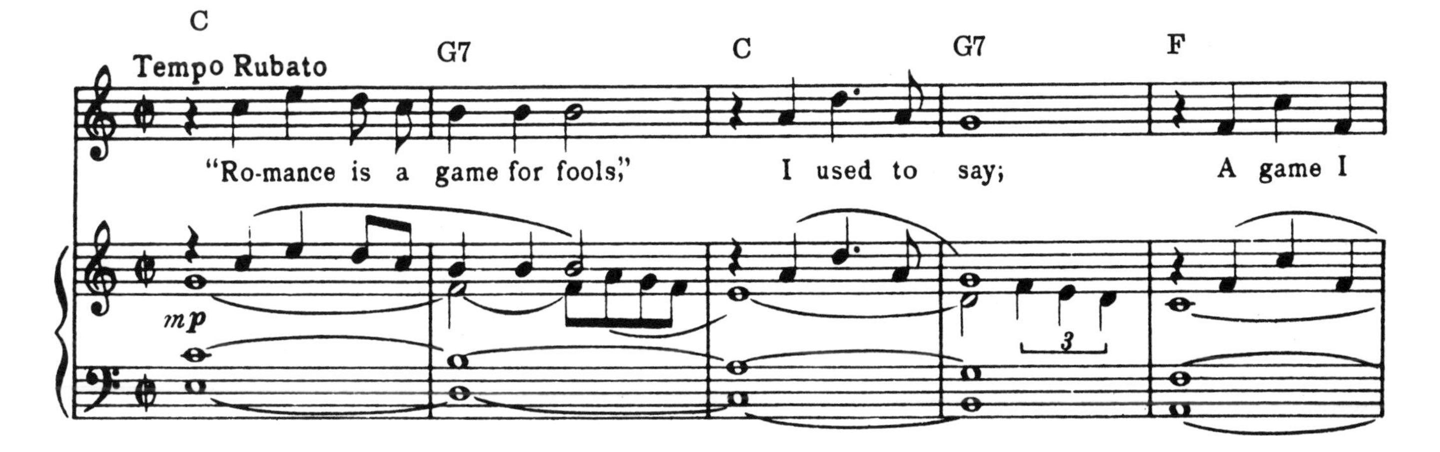

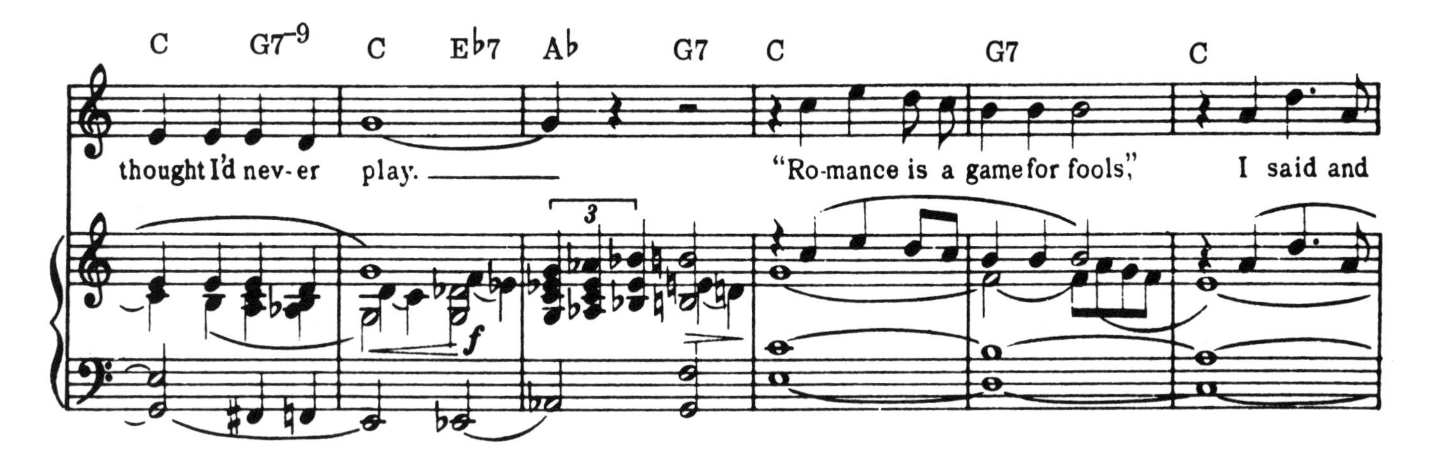

Dm7
G7
C
Am7
Fools Rush In
where an-gels fear to
tread,
and so I come to

Dm7
G7
C
you, my love,
my heart a-bove my
head.
Though I

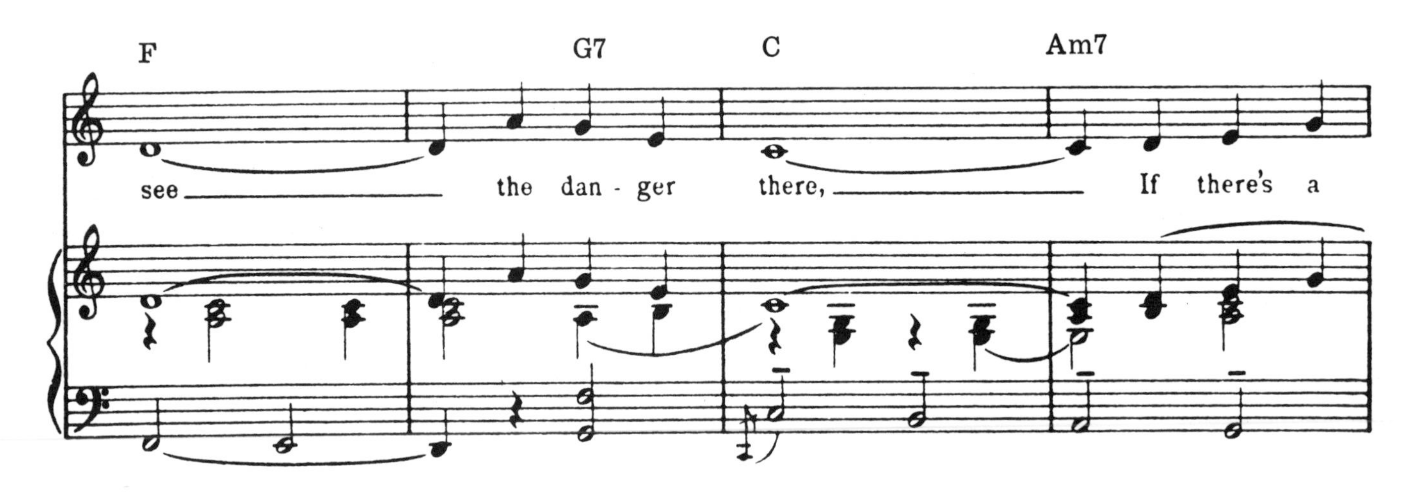
F
G7
C
Am7
see
the dan-ger
there,
If there's a

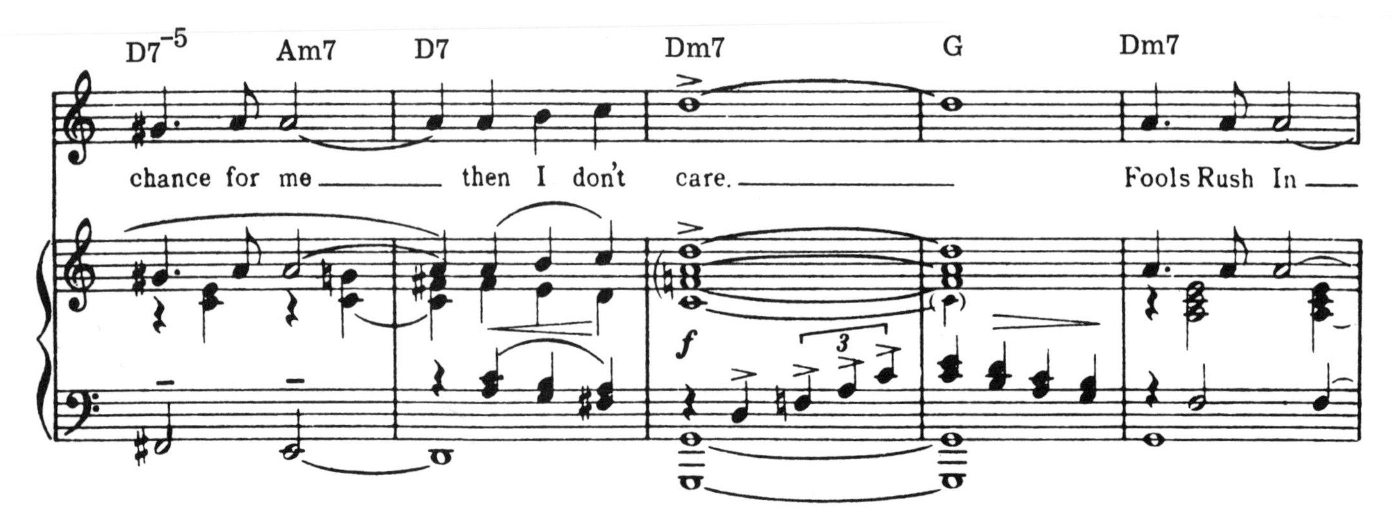
D7-5
Am7
D7
Dm7
G
Dm7
chance for me
then I don't
care.
Fools Rush In
f

G7 C Am7 Dm7
where wise men nev - er go, but wise men nev - er fall in love

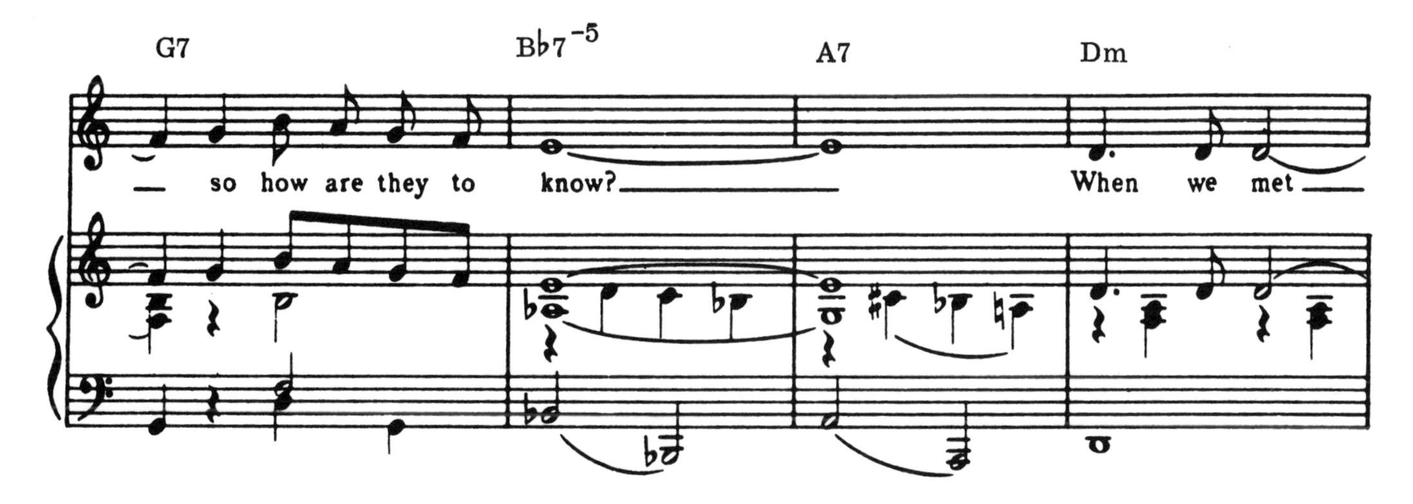
G7 B♭7⁻⁵ A7 Dm
so how are they to know? When we met

Fm6 C Am Dm
I felt my life be - gin; So o - pen up your heart, and let
ff

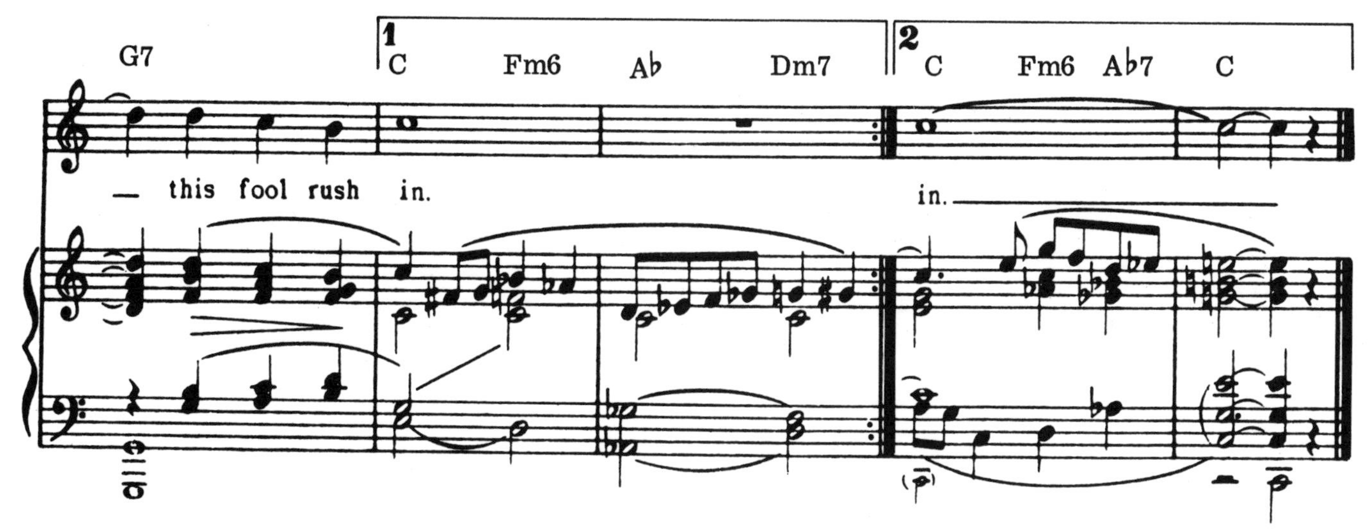
G7 1 C Fm6 A♭ Dm7 2 C Fm6 A♭7 C
this fool rush in. in.

AGAIN

WORDS BY
DORCAS COCHRAN

MUSIC BY
LIONEL NEWMAN

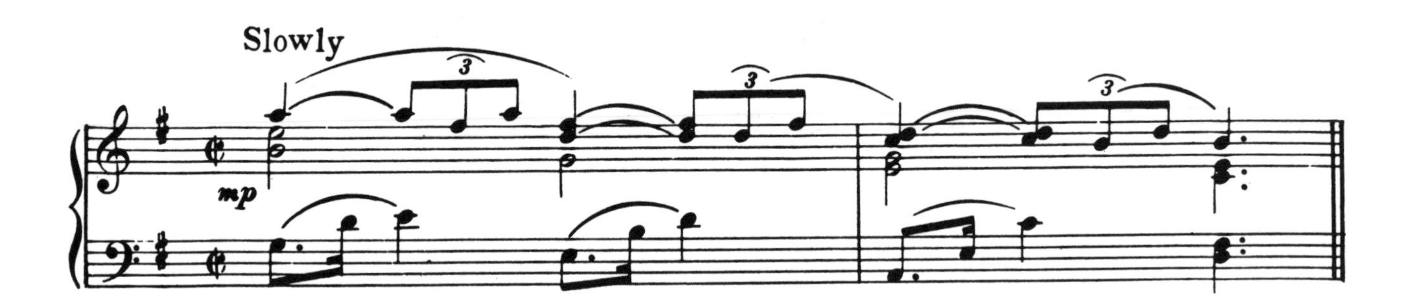

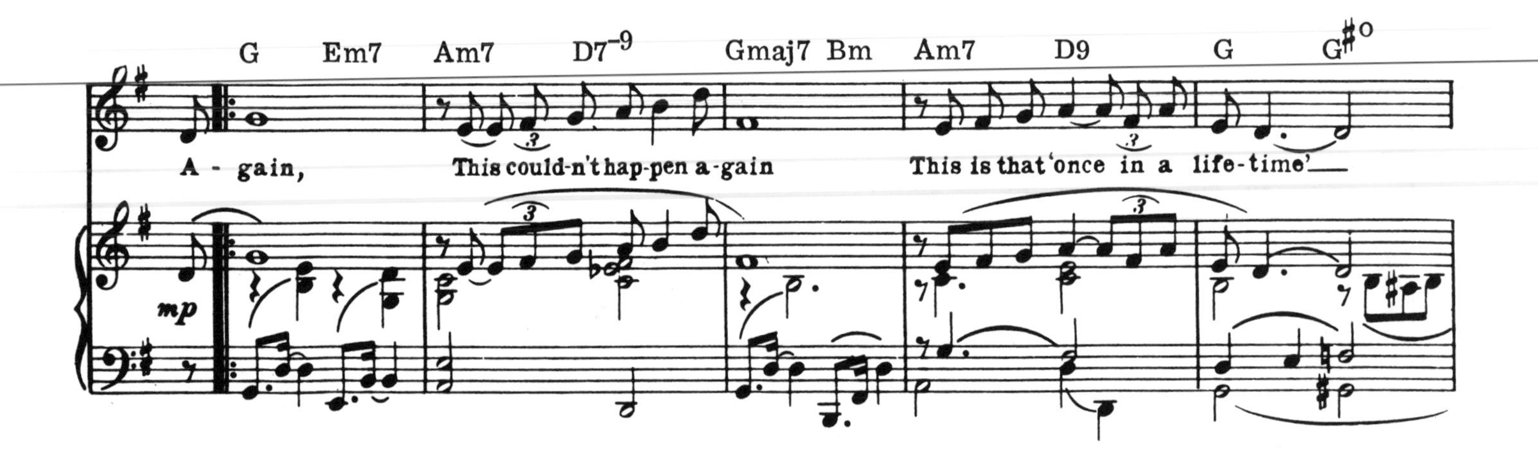

G G+ G6 G7 C E♭9 D7-9 G Gmaj7
sud - den-ly be mine Mine to hold as I'm hold - ing you now and yet nev - er so

G9 C E♭9 Am7 D7 Am7 D7-9
near Mine to have when the now and the here dis - ap - pear What mat - ters, dear, for

G Em7 Am7 D7-9 Gmaj7 Bm Am7 D9 G G#o
when This does - n't hap - pen a - gain We'll have this mo - ment for - ev - er

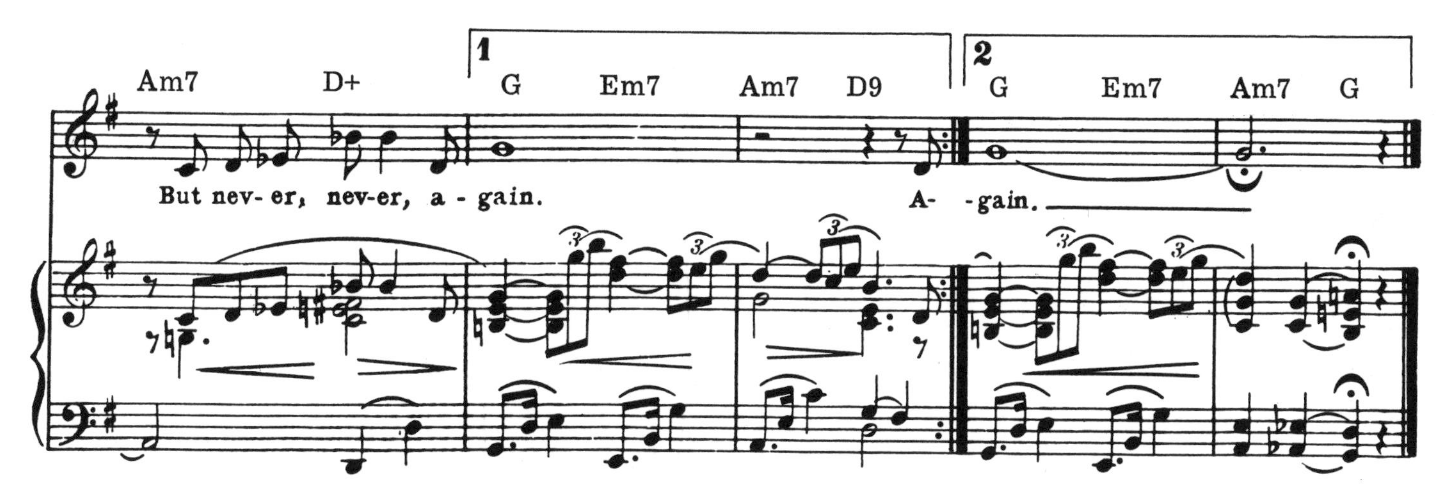
1
2
Am7 D+ G Em7 Am7 D9 G Em7 Am7 G
But nev - er, nev - er, a - gain. A - gain.

ALWAYS IN MY HEART

LYRICS BY
KIM GANNON

MUSIC BY
ERNESTO LECUONA

F F#o Gm7 G7-5 C7 Cm7 F7
time. please be - lieve me when I say:

REFRAIN
B♭ F+ B♭ F7+
You are al - ways in my heart ev - en tho' you're far a -

B♭ F+ B♭
way, I can hear the mu - sic of the song of
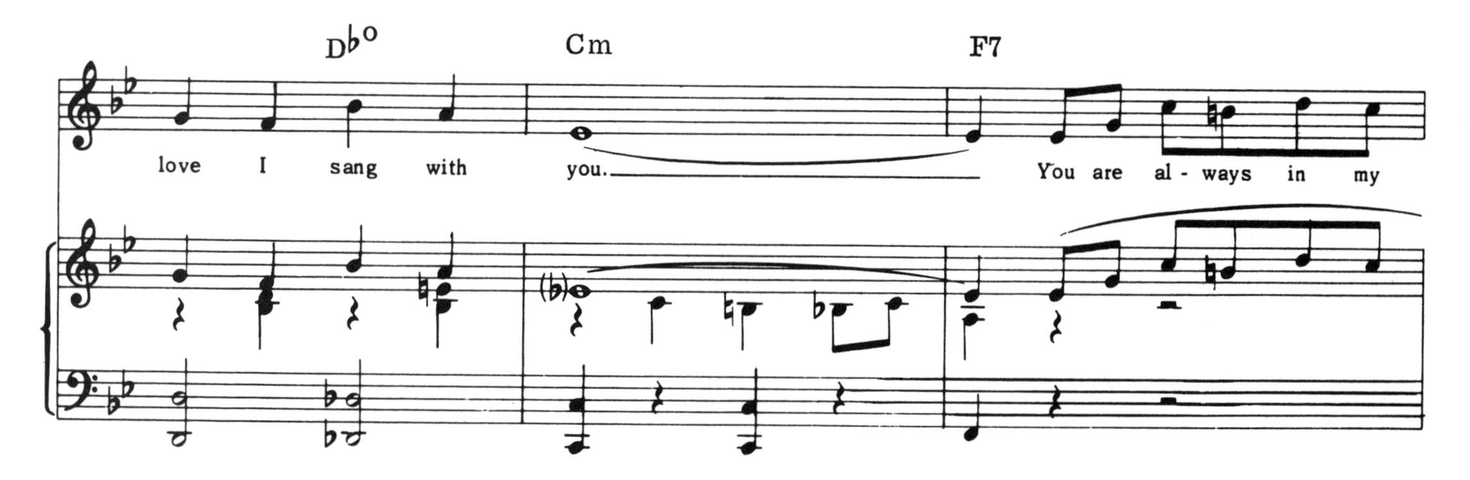
D♭o Cm F7
love I sang with you. You are al - ways in my

Cm7
E♭m6
F7
heart
and when skies a - bove are grey

Cm7
F7
E°
I re - mem - ber that you care
and then and there the sun breaks

B♭
F+
thru.
Just be - fore I go to sleep

B♭
F7+
B♭
F+
B♭
there's a ren - dez - vous I keep
and the dream I al - ways

Fm6 G7 Cm
meet helps me for - get we're far a - part,

E♭m6
I don't know ex - act - ly when dear but I'm sure we'll meet a -

B♭ B♭o F7 A F7
gain dear and my dar - ling till we do you are al - ways in my

1 B♭ F7+ 2 B♭
heart. You are al - ways in my heart.